What Else Can I Pl
Violin
Grade Four

International MUSIC Publications

Series Editor: Miranda Steel

Music arranged and processed by
Barnes Music Engraving Ltd
East Sussex TN22 4HA, England

Cover design by Headline Publicity

Published 2000

Introduction

In this *What Else Can I Play?* collection you'll find eighteen popular tunes that are both challenging and entertaining.

The pieces have been carefully selected and arranged to create ideal supplementary material for young violinists who are either working towards or have recently taken a Grade Four violin examination.

As the student progresses through the volume, technical demands increase and new concepts are introduced which reflect the requirements of the major examination boards. Suggestions and guidelines on bowing, fingering, dynamics and tempo are given for each piece, together with technical tips and performance notes.

Pupils will experience a wide variety of music, ranging from classical and jazz through to showtunes and popular songs, leading to a greater awareness of musical styles.

Whether it's for light relief from examination preparation, or to reinforce the understanding of new concepts, this collection will enthuse and encourage all young violinists.

Daydream believer

Words and Music by John Stewart

4

Try to remember

Music by Harvey Schmidt

It's alright with me

Words and Music by Cole Porter

Love's got a hold on my heart

Words and Music by Andrew Frampton and Pete Waterman

Talk to the animals

Words and Music by Leslie Bricusse

Close to you (they long to be)

Music by Burt Bacharach

Music to watch girls by

Words and Music by Anthony Verona and Sid Ramin

April in Paris

Music by Vernon Duke

Star Wars (main title)

Music by John Williams

I got rhythm

Music and Lyrics by George Gershwin and Ira Gershwin

In the mood

Music by Joe Garland

Singin' in the rain

Music by Nacio Herb Brown

What Else Can I Play?
Violin
Grade Four

Daydream believer

Words and Music by John Stewart

'Daydream Believer' became a top ten hit for The Monkees in 1967. The band was conceived as a television show about a struggling pop group, and were more of a popular than critical success, especially when it was discovered that they did not play on their early records. Carole King, Neil Diamond and Harry Nilsson all wrote for them at different times.

This melody should be played with lots of expression. Use nice long bows for a good tone but keep the tune flowing, as if you were singing the line.

Try to remember

Music by Harvey Schmidt

This is perhaps the best known song from *The Fantasticks*, one of the longest running American stage musicals. It opened on the 3rd of May 1960 and ran for over 12,000 performances. The song has been recorded by the actor Edward Woodward, among others.

This is a beautiful melody and needs to be played in an expressive way. Take careful note of the suggested dynamics because these will give your performance added interest. Use long bows to help achieve a good tone and you might want to use third position from bars 34 to the end to avoid difficult string crossing with the bow.

It's alright with me

Words and Music by Cole Porter

Despite interrupting his career to join the French Foreign Legion during the First World War, Cole Porter's talent as a jobbing songwriter foreshadowed his later success. 'It's Alright With Me' from his smash hit musical 'Can Can' has been recorded by over forty different artists, from Harry Connick Jnr. to the Zombies.

Try to play this melody as smoothly as you can using long bows. In bars 12 and 46 (where the E goes to D sharp and back to E) try keeping the first finger on the string all the time as this will produce a slide effect. This is something you will have to practise, taking care to keep the rhythm steady.

Love's got a hold on my heart

Words and Music by Andrew Frampton and Pete Waterman

This was a hit for the pop quintet Steps. Pete Waterman, who co-wrote it, firmly established himself as a writer/producer in the 80s with Matt Aitken and Mike Stock as Stock, Aitken and Waterman. The trio modelled themselves on the Motown hit factory of the 60s.

This is a melody that needs to be played with lots of feeling and you might want to use some vibrato. When you first start to learn this piece, try counting in quavers (eight to the bar), as it should help you with some of the more difficult cross rhythms.

Talk to the animals

Words and Music by Leslie Bricusse

Leslie Bricusse wrote both the script and song score for the film of *Dr. Dolittle* in 1967. It was revived as a West End musical over thirty years on with Philip Schofield in the lead role. Bricusse collaborated with Anthony Newley (who was in the film) on a number of projects, including the words of the title song to the James Bond movie *Goldfinger*.

This is a playful melody in three sections. The first is similar to the third and the middle section (from bar 13) creates a contrast. This section should be very legato; use nice long bows and try out your vibrato.

Close to you (they long to be)

Music by Burt Bacharach

'Close To You' was the first hit for the brother-and-sister duo, the Carpenters. It was written by Burt Bacharach and Hal David, one of of the most successful musical partnerships in the history of popular music.

This piece has two main themes. The first should be expressive and lyrical. Play the notes in the second section (from bar 21) a little shorter to create a contrast. Don't forget to make the most of the crescendo in bar 26.

Music to watch girls by

Words and Music by Anthony Verona and Sid Ramin

First made popular by Andy Williams in the 60s, 'Music To Watch Girls By' was revived more recently for a car advertisement on television. In 1945, Williams dubbed Lauren Becall's singing voice in her first film with Humphrey Bogart, *To Have And Have Not*.

You can give the melody a bit of a lift by playing the notes very slightly staccato. There is definitely humour in this tune, so try smiling while you are playing.

April in Paris

Music by Vernon Duke

Vernon Duke is best known for his musical and film scores, although he also developed a style for choral works, operas, ballets and chamber works. This piece became known for accompanying the famous scene in the 1953 film, where Doris Day and Ray Bolger dance in the street after their romantic day is interrupted by wind and rain.

You should have a relaxed approach to this piece. Start at the point of the bow and use long bows – but lightly: don't press down too much. Stretch out the triplets as much as you can.

Star Wars (main title)

Music by John Williams

Son of a studio musician, John Williams became a multi-instrumentalist as a boy and broke into film work early in his career. He has been prolific, earning more than twenty-five Oscar nominations. He scored Ronald Reagan's last film, *The Killers* in 1964.

This is a march with a very striking tune that should be played majestically. Keep the triplets nice and crisp using separate bows and make the most of the big finish. Feel the force!

I got rhythm

Music and Lyrics by George Gershwin and Ira Gershwin

'I Got Rhythm' is from the Broadway show *Girl Crazy* (1932). It marked Ethel Merman's rise from nightclub singer to Broadway star. She was in a supporting role and it was the only song she had, but she made her presence felt, holding a high C for 16 bars in the coda. Never a retiring character, Cole Porter described her as being like a "brass band going by".

As the title would suggest, rhythm has a particularly important part to play in this piece! Use the tip of the bow and play the dotted notes neatly and in time. You could accent the beginning of some of the notes that are syncopated. In places like bar 40, where two consecutive notes are played with the same finger, you can have fun with jazz style slides.

In the mood

Music by Joe Garland

Although it is most widely remembered as an instrumental piece popularised by Joe Loss and particularly Glenn Miller, 'In The Mood' was written in 1939 by Joe Garland, a saxophonist and arranger for dance and jazz bands. The original version had lyrics and was a success in its own right.

Play this with a crisp rhythmical bow stroke and see if you can get everyone's feet tapping! Make the most of the accents as they are very much part of what makes this melody swing.

Singin' in the rain

Music by Nacio Herb Brown

Although 'Singin' In The Rain' is best remembered as the title song of the 1952 film, it had been used in two earlier films, *Hollywood Revue* and *Little Nelly Kelly*. In addition to songwriting, Arthur Freed was an important producer of film musicals for the MGM studio, and revived it for Gene Kelly's memorable dance number.

As the title suggests, this is a singing melody which provides a great opportunity for you to try out your vibrato. Keep the dotted rhythms crisp and fairly short using the tip to the middle of the bow.

The Pink Panther theme

Music by Henry Mancini

This was the title music of the 1964 film starring Peter Sellers. Henry Mancini, who wrote it, was a pianist and arranger with the Glenn Miller orchestra. He wrote a lot of film music, including the song 'Moon River' from *Breakfast at Tiffany's* (1961), for which he won an Oscar.

This is a very moody piece of music so pay attention to all of the dynamics. Keep the dotted quavers fairly short. Leave the finger on the string where the same finger is used to play consecutive notes – this should produce a sliding effect. Enjoy the last note!

Toreador's song

Music by Georges Bizet

'Toreador's Song' is taken from *Carmen* by Georges Bizet. It was his last theatrical work of note. When it was first staged in 1875 the audience was indifferent and the press was scandalised by the unapologetic caprices of the heroine.

This piece is a proper march. Everything should be bang on: rhythm, tempo, staccati. The dotted rhythms should be snappy and the triplets should be crisp.

Coronation Street

Music by Eric Spear

Coronation Street was first shown at 7pm on the 9th of December 1960 and is the longest running TV show in the United Kingdom. A number of famous names have cropped up on the programme, including Joan Collins, Davy Jones (later of The Monkees) and Martin Shaw (Doyle from *The Professionals*).

This is a tune that we have all heard at some time or other. Knowledge of the melody will help your interpretation. A slightly lazy style would be good; make the most of the triplets and don't make the dotted notes too snappy. Use just the upper half of the bow and exaggerate the rubato section at the end.

In the hall of the mountain king

Music by Grieg

'In The Hall Of The Mountain King' is part of the *Peer Gynt Suite*, which was commissioned by Henrik Ibsen as incidental music to his play *Peer Gynt*. The musical suite was first published as a piano duet.

The notes need to be kept very short in this piece. You could try playing them off the bow, but otherwise the bow needs to be stopped after each note. This allows plenty of time to retake the bow on a down (as in bar 6). In bars 47 and 48 you should try the suggested half position.

Mexican hat dance

Traditional

This is a piece of traditional Mexican dance music. The first performance on record was at the Coliseo in Mexico City in 1790. It appeared more recently in the 1945 film *Anchors Aweigh* starring Frank Sinatra and Gene Kelly.

You will find this music great fun to play. Don't forget that it is a dance so play with a strong sense of rhythm, giving the rests their full value. It needs to be played at a very sprightly pace.

The greatest love of all

Music by Michael Masser

This song was written as part of the soundtrack for a 1977 film called 'The Greatest' which was about the life of Muhammad Ali, who played himself. In the film it was sung by George Benson, but has since been recorded by Whitney Houston.

The violin part is taken from the vocal line and is fairly syncopated throughout. Use light bows and try to relax while playing. Expression is important with this piece because of its romantic nature.

Reproduced and printed by
Halstan & Co. Ltd., Amersham, Bucks., England

You can be the featured soloist with
TAKE THE LEAD

Collect these titles, each with demonstration and full backing tracks on CD.

90s Hits	Movie Hits	TV Themes	Christmas Songs	The Blues Brothers
The Air That I Breathe (Simply Red)	**Because You Loved Me** (Up Close And Personal)	**Coronation Street**	**The Christmas Song (Chestnuts Roasting On An Open Fire)**	**She Caught The Katy And Left Me A Mule To Ride**
Angels (Robbie Williams)	**Blue Monday** (The Wedding Singer)	**I'll Be There For You (theme from Friends)**	**Frosty The Snowman**	**Gimme Some Lovin'**
How Do I Live (LeAnn Rimes)	**(Everything I Do) I Do It For You** (Robin Hood: Prince Of Thieves)	**Match Of The Day**	**Have Yourself A Merry Little Christmas**	**Shake A Tail Feather**
I Don't Want To Miss A Thing (Aerosmith)	**I Don't Want To Miss A Thing** (Armageddon)	**(Meet) The Flintstones**	**Little Donkey**	**Everybody Needs Somebody To Love**
I'll Be There For You (The Rembrandts)	**I Will Always Love You** (The Bodyguard)	**Men Behaving Badly**	**Rudolph The Red-Nosed Reindeer**	**The Old Landmark**
My Heart Will Go On (Celine Dion)	**Star Wars (Main Title)** (Star Wars)	**Peak Practice**	**Santa Claus Is Comin' To Town**	**Think**
Something About The Way You Look Tonight (Elton John)	**The Wind Beneath My Wings** (Beaches)	**The Simpsons**	**Sleigh Ride**	**Minnie The Moocher**
Frozen (Madonna)	**You Can Leave Your Hat On** (The Full Monty)	**The X-Files**	**Winter Wonderland**	**Sweet Home Chicago**
Order ref: 6725A – Flute	Order ref: 6908A – Flute	Order ref: 7003A – Flute	Order ref: 7022A – Flute	Order ref: 7079A - Flute
Order ref: 6726A – Clarinet	Order ref: 6909A – Clarinet	Order ref: 7004A – Clarinet	Order ref: 7023A – Clarinet	Order ref: 7080A - Clarinet
Order ref: 6727A – Alto Saxophone	Order ref: 6910A – Alto Saxophone	Order ref: 7005A – Alto Saxophone	Order ref: 7024A – Alto Saxophone	Order ref: 7081A - Alto Saxophone
Order ref: 6728A – Violin	Order ref: 6911A –Tenor Saxophone	Order ref: 7006A – Violin	Order ref: 7025A – Violin	Order ref: 7082A - Tenor Saxophone
	Order ref: 6912A – Violin		Order ref: 7026A – Piano	Order ref: 7083A - Trumpet
			Order ref: 7027A – Drums	Order ref: 7084A - Violin

Out Of Reach

Words & Music by Gabrielle & Jonathan Shorten

Close your eyes
Give me your hand, darlin
Do you feel my heart beating
Do you understand
Do you feel the same
Or am i only dreaming
Is this burning, an eternal flame

I believe
It's meant to be, darling
I watch you when you are sleeping
You belong to me
Do you feel the same
Or am i only dreaming
Is this burning, an eternal flame

Say my name, sun shines through the rain
Of our life so lonely
Then come and ease the pain
I don't want to lose this feeling, oooh

Oh oh

Say my name, sun shines through the rain
Of our life so lonely
Now come and ease the pain
I don't want to lose this feeling, oooh

Close your eyes
Give me your hand, darling
Do you feel my heart beating
Do you understand
Do you feel the same
Am i only dreaming
Or is this burning, an eternal flame

Close your eyes
Give me your hand, darling
Do you feel my heart beating
Do you understand (do you understand)
Do you feel the same
Am I only dreaming (dreaming)
Or is this burning, an eternal flame

Close your eyes
Give me your hand, darling (Give me your hand)
Do you feel my heart beating
Do you understand (Give me your hand)
Do you feel the same
Am I only dreaming (dreaming)
Is this burning, an eternal flame

The Pink Panther theme

Music by Henry Mancini

Toreador's song

Music by Georges Bizet

Coronation Street

Music by Eric Spear

Moderately slow (♩ = 88)

In the hall of the mountain king

Music by Grieg

Mexican hat dance

Traditional

The greatest love of all

Music by Michael Masser

Slowly, with feeling (♩ = 70)

Why not extend your repertoire with:

Congratulations!
You've Just Passed Grade 1

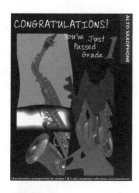

6796A
Alto Saxophone

6797A
Clarinet

6794A
Flute

6798A
Piano

6795A
Violin

- Features standard repertoire which is ideal for Grades 1-2.
- Available for clarinet, alto saxophone, flute and violin with piano accompaniment; and piano solo.
- A wide variety of titles from jazz to pop, and from classical to folk.
- Fifteen great progressive titles in each book.

Series includes: *Angels – Autumn Leaves – Blueberry Hill – Bye Bye Blackbird – Don't Bring Lu Lu – The Hippopotamus Song – How Do I Live – I Don't Want To Miss A Thing – I'm Forever Blowing Bubbles – I've Got No Strings – Jeepers Creepers – My Heart Will Go On*